The baby giraffe had not seen the elephants.

‘My family will help you find them,’ she said.

The baby giraffe took Alfie to meet her mother and father. 'I am looking for the elephants,' said Alfie. 'I have lost them.'

The big giraffes stretched up. They were very tall.

They looked all over the grassy land of Africa.

‘The elephants are over there by the trees,’ said the father giraffe. ‘We will take you to them.’

The giraffes set off with Alfie to meet the elephants by the trees. Alfie was feeling excited as they came near.

He saw his father, the biggest elephant. He saw his mother too. The big elephants came to meet him.

‘Oh, Alfie,’ said his mother. ‘We lost you. We went back to look for you but you had gone.’

Soon all the elephants were around Alfie. They raised their trunks and gave a cheer. Alfie was happy to be with them again.